Name _____

Draw a line to connect the matching letters.

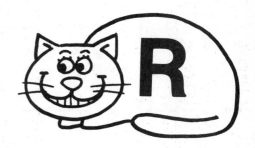

I

Circle the letters that match the first letter in each row.

b	(b)	h	b	b	d	b	h
f	t	f	r	f	t	f	f
h	h	h	k	b	h	h	b
t	f	t	t	f	l	t	t
k	k	k	h	k	t	k	k
d	d	d	h	d	b	d	b
o	o	c	a	o	o	c	o

FS-2654 Kindergarten Workbook-Book Two

Draw a line to connect the matching letters.

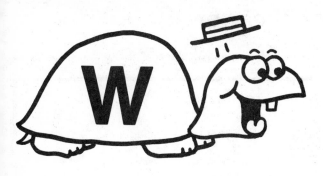

Circle the letters that match the first letter in each row.

a	a o a b a e a
c	o c e c c a c
e	e c e o e c e
m	n m r u m m r
r	r m r n u r n
n	n r u n m r n
u	u m n u r n u

4

Write the missing letter.

c _ e   _ f g   t u _   q _ s

c d _   i j _   _ x y   a _ c

k _ m   _ t u   a b _   d e _

_ n o      t _ v

Name _____

The Juggler

Cut and paste the pins in ABC order. Color the picture.

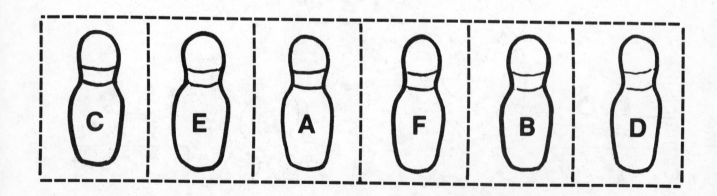

Name _____

Connect the dots from a to z!

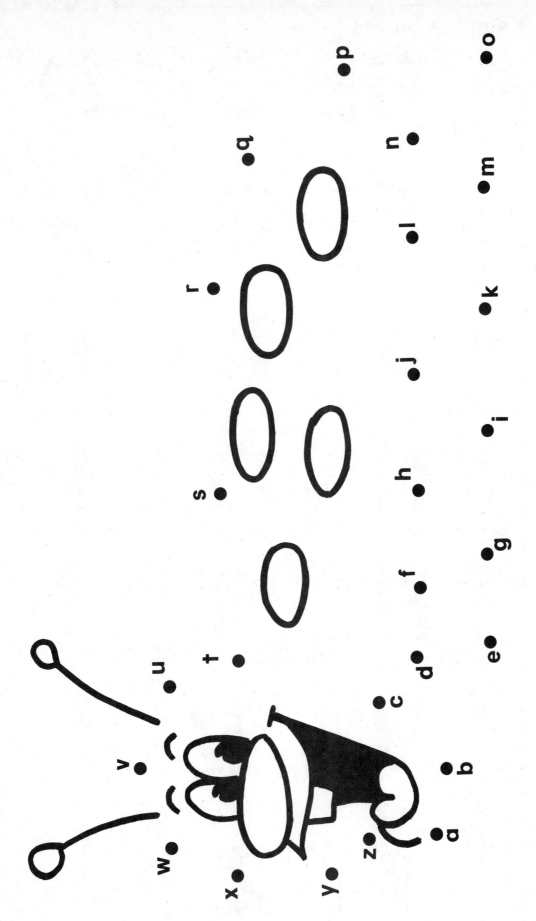

Copy the sample letters.

A A B B C C D D

E E F F G G H H

I I J J K K L L

M M N N O O P P

Q Q R R S S T T

U U V V W W

X X Y Y Z Z

©Frank Schaffer Publications, Inc.

FS-2654 Kindergarten Workbook-Book Two

Name _____

Skill: Alphabet sequencing

Write the missing letter.

_ b c
_ t u
_ s t
_ l m

_ n o
_ w x
_ e f
_ p q

_ y z
_ c d
_ f g
_ o p

_ m n

_ j k

©Frank Schaffer Publications, Inc.

9

FS-2654 Kindergarten Workbook-Book Two

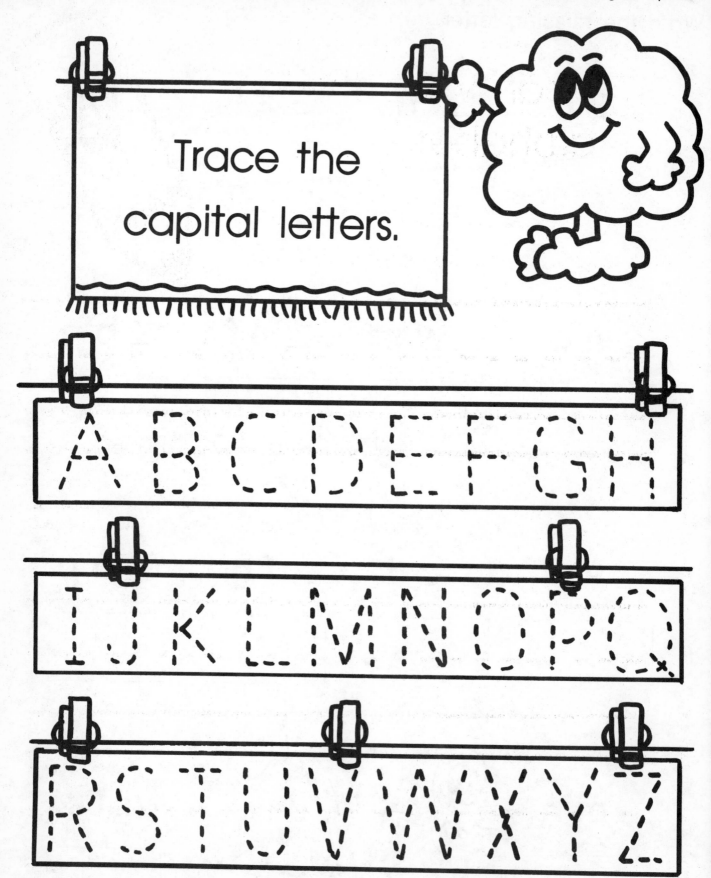

Trace the capital letters.

A B C D E F G H

I J K L M N O P Q

R S T U V W X Y Z

FS-2654 Kindergarten Workbook-Book Two

I can write the alphabet.

FS-2654 Kindergarten Workbook-Book Two

Connect the dots in ABC order to find out which animal is in the cage.

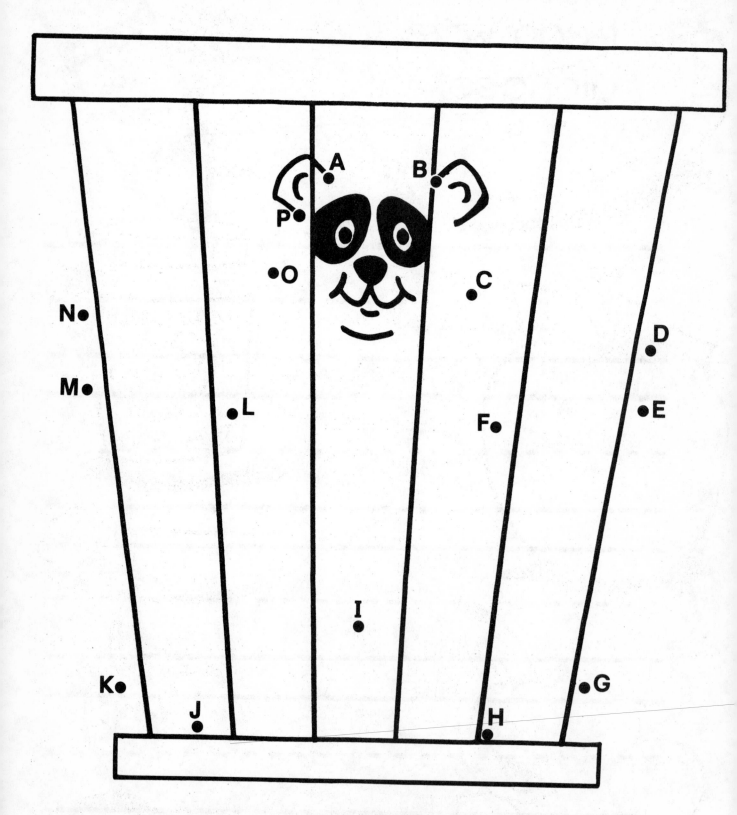

12

Color the things that are
usually red.

red

FS-2654   Kindergarten Workbook-Book Two

Cut and paste.

| yellow | yellow | yellow |

Color the things that are usually blue.

blue

FS-2654 Kindergarten Workbook-Book Two

Cut and paste.

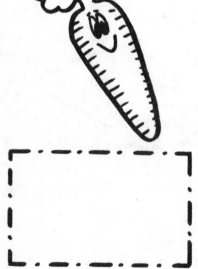

| orange | orange | orange |

Color the things that are usually black.

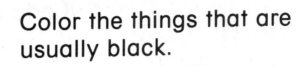

black

INK

17

Cut and paste.

| green | green | green |

18

FS-2654 Kindergarten Workbook-Book Two

Color the things that are usually purple.

purple

FS-2654 Kindergarten Workbook-Book Two

Color the things that are
usually brown.

brown

Color the pictures.
Trace each word.

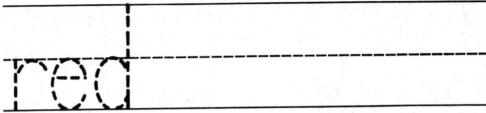

red

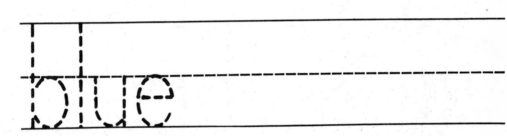

blue

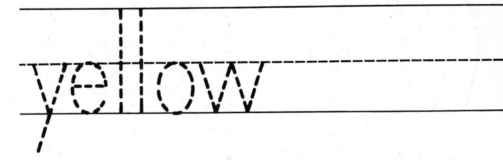

yellow

black

FS-2654 Kindergarten Workbook-Book Two

Color the pictures.
Trace each word.

green

orange

purple

brown

Circle the correct number in each box.

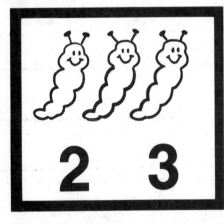

FS-2654 Kindergarten Workbook-Book Two

Name _____

Circle the correct number in each box.

©Frank Schaffer Publications, Inc.

FS-2654 Kindergarten Workbook-Book Two

Name _____

How many?

_____ _____ _____ _____

_____ _____ _____ _____

_____ _____ _____ _____

_____ _____

How many?

_____ _____ _____ _____

  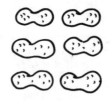 

_____ _____ _____ _____

_____ _____ _____ _____

_____ _____ _____

How many?

_____   _____   _____   _____

_____   _____   _____   _____

_____   _____   _____   _____

_____   _____

FS-2654   Kindergarten Workbook-Book Two

Circle the larger number in each box.

3 4	2 3
1 5	4 3

5 4	3 4	5 6
6 4	8 6	7 5
7 8	9 8	6 8
4 9	5 2	3 7

FS-2654 Kindergarten Workbook-Book Two

Name _____

Circle the correct numbers in each box.

| 9 | 9 | 7 | 9 | 6 | 9 | 9 | 7 | 6 |

| 3 | 5 | 3 | 2 | 3 | 5 | 3 | 3 | 2 |

| 2 | 2 | 3 | 7 | 2 | 5 | 2 | 9 | 2 |

| 5 | 6 | 5 | 5 | 2 | 2 | 5 | 8 | 5 |

| 6 | 9 | 6 | 9 | 6 | 2 | 6 | 5 | 6 |

| 7 | 2 | 7 | 9 | 7 | 7 | 1 | 7 | 2 |

| 8 | 6 | 8 | 6 | 8 | 9 | 8 | 9 | 8 |

Name _____

How many?

_____ _____ _____ _____

  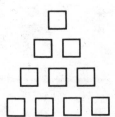 

_____ _____ _____ _____

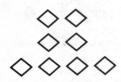

_____ _____ _____ _____

_____

30

Name _____

Look at the numbers! Draw lines to match the pairs.

31

Name _____

How many?

   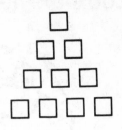

_____ _____ _____ _____

 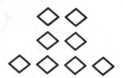

_____ _____ _____ _____

_____ _____ _____ _____

_____   _____

Name _____

Write the missing numeral.

3,__,5	8,__,10	2,__,4	6,__,8	4,__,6
___	___	___	___	___

7,__,9	0,__,2	4,__,6	3,__,5	2,__,4
___	___	___	___	___

6,__,8	8,__,10	1,__,3	5,__,7	0,__,2
___	___	___	___	___

FS-2654   Kindergarten Workbook-Book Two

Name _____

Write the numeral.

five	six	two	four	one
____	____	____	____	____

six	one	three	six	two
____	____	____	____	____

five	four	two	five	three
____	____	____	____	____

FS-2654 Kindergarten Workbook-Book Two

Name _____

Write the numerals.

seven	one	four	six	two
____	____	____	____	____

five	three	eight	ten	four
____	____	____	____	____

five	seven	nine	six	eight
____	____	____	____	____

The Flying Trapeze

Color the pictures that go with the first one in each row.

Name

Trace all ----- with a yellow crayon, then red, then blue. Follow the arrows.

FS-2654 Kindergarten Workbook-Book Two

The Ringmaster

Help the ringmaster get ready for the show. Color and cut out all the pictures and paste them in the right places.

Trace all ------ with a yellow crayon, then red, then blue. Follow the arrows.

The Balancing Act

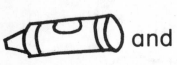 and  and  =

FS-2654 Kindergarten Workbook-Book Two

Skills: Review-Circles, Straight lines, Diagonals

Trace all ----- with a yellow crayon, then red, then blue. Follow the arrows.

©Frank Schaffer Publications, Inc.

FS-2654 Kindergarten Workbook-Book Two

 and  and  =

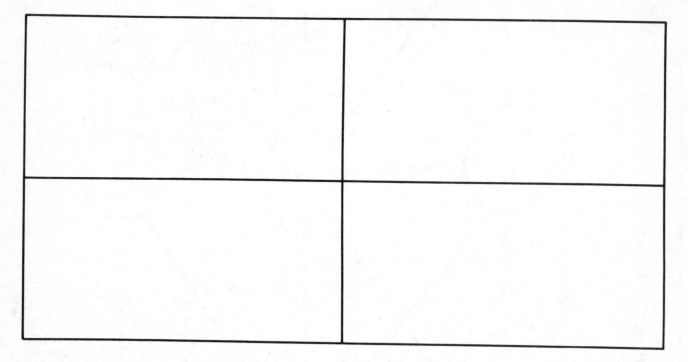

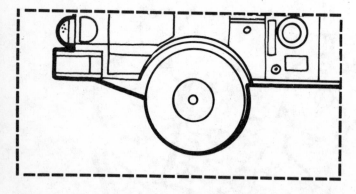

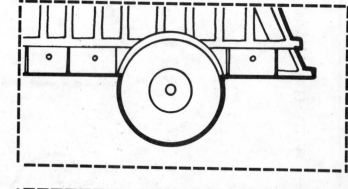

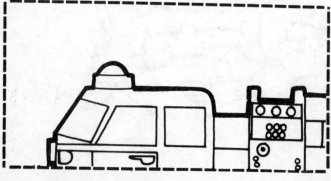

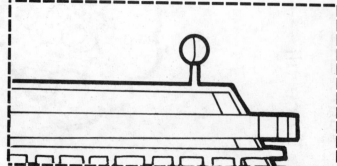

Trace all ------ with a yellow crayon, then red, then blue.
Follow the arrows.

FS-2654 Kindergarten Workbook-Book Two

Three-Ring Circus

Cut and paste each picture in the right ring. Color the picture.

Name _____

Trace all ----- with a yellow crayon, then red, then blue. Follow the arrows.

The lions live in a big den. Cut out the lions and paste them in their den.

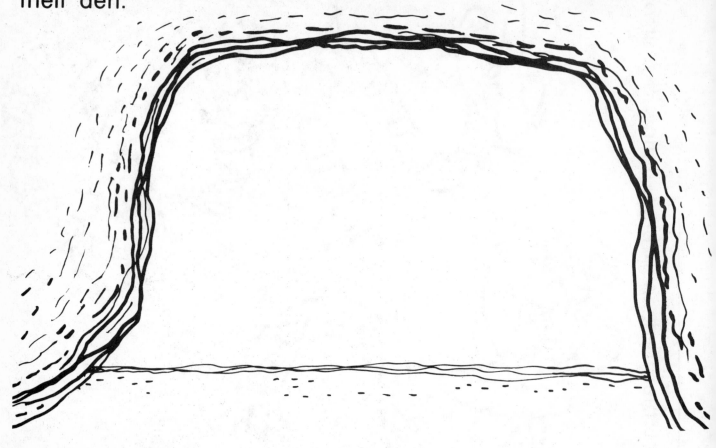

46

FS-2654   Kindergarten Workbook-Book Two

Name _____

Trace all ----- with a yellow crayon, then red, then blue. Follow the arrows.

Skill: Over and under curves

©Frank Schaffer Publications, Inc.   FS-2654 Kindergarten Workbook-Book Two

Skills: Left circles, Straight lines—left to right

Trace all ----- with a yellow crayon, then red, then blue. Follow the arrows.

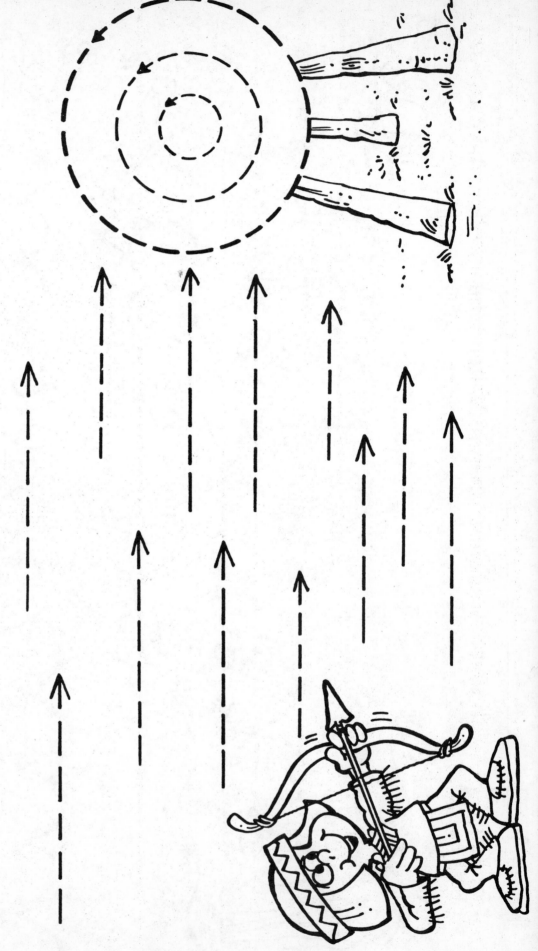

48